iPrimary

Global Citizenship

Year 1 Workbook

Published by Pearson Education Limited, 80 Strand, London, WC2R 0RL.
www.pearson.com/international-schools

Copies of official specifications for all Pearson Edexcel qualifications may be found on the website:
https://qualifications.pearson.com

Text © Pearson Education Limited 2022
Project managed and edited by Just Content Limited
Designed and typeset by PDQ Digital Media Solutions Limited
Picture research by SPi
Original illustrations © Pearson Education Limited 2022
Cover design © Pearson Education Limited 2022

The right of Charlotte Guillain to be identified as the author of this work has been asserted by her in accordance with the Copyright, Designs and Patents Act 1988.

First published 2022

24 23 22
10 9 8 7 6 5 4 3 2 1

British Library Cataloguing in Publication Data
A catalogue record for this book is available from the British Library

ISBN 978 1 292 39674 3

Printed in Slovakia by Neografia

Acknowledgements
The publisher would like to thank the following for their kind permission to reproduce their photographs:

Cover acknowledgements
Shutterstock: Janna7/Shutterstock

Photos acknowledgements
123RF: Pavlo Vakhrushev/123RF 38; Jan Hof/123RF 43; breakingthewalls/123RF 43; zerbor/123RF 45, 47; hannesthirion/123RF 64; **Alamy Stock Photo:** WaterFrame/Alamy Stock Photo 38; Gary Dublanko/Alamy Stock Photo 38; Gerard Lacz/mauritius images GmbH/Alamy Stock Photo 38; Francois Gohier/VWPics/Alamy Stock Photo 64; Igor Sinitsyn/Alamy Stock Photo 64; Cultura Creative RF/Alamy Stock Photo 67; blickwinkel/McPHOTO/RUN/Alamy Stock Photo 52; **Shutterstock:** haveseen/Shutterstock 38; Andrey Solovev/Shutterstock 43; Sarah2/Shutterstock 43; Michal Kaco/Shutterstock 43; Fotofermer/Shutterstock 43; Henk Bentlage/Shutterstock 43; Yeti studio/Shutterstock 43; BOKYPORNAREE GALLERY/Shutterstock 52; IVAN ABORNEV/Shutterstock 64; buteo/Shutterstock 67; Signature Message/Shutterstock 67; Four Oaks/Shutterstock 67; Matt Jeppson. Shutterstock 67; REDPIXEL.PL/Shutterstock 93; Brovkina/Shutterstock 93; Ian 2010/Shutterstock 93; anaken2012/Shutterstock 93; S-F/Shutterstock 93; Valeriy Lebedev/Shutterstock 93; REDPIXEL.PL/Shutterstock 95; Valeriy Lebedev/Shutterstock 95; Brovkina/Shutterstock 95; Saikorn. Shutterstock 95; Dmitry Pichugin/Shutterstock 63; Vlad61/Shutterstock 63; Tarpan/Shutterstock 64; Fotos593/Shutterstock 64; StevenRussellSmithPhotos/Shutterstock 52; FotoDuets/Shutterstock 93; Chase B/Shutterstock 52; Michael PotterII/Shutterstock 67; Andrey Pavlov/Shutterstock 38

All other images © Pearson Education

Contents

Welcome to Global Citizenship!

We hope you will find this book useful as you approach the exciting subject of Global Citizenship! This book will form a key part of your journey to becoming a Global Citizen. It will help you understand the wider world, your place in it, how you can engage with issues locally and globally and how you can enact positive change.

Objective
This is what you will know or be able to do by the end of the session.

We will learn
This is what you will be learning in the session.

Key vocabulary
These are important words to know.

Information
This is an introduction to the session.

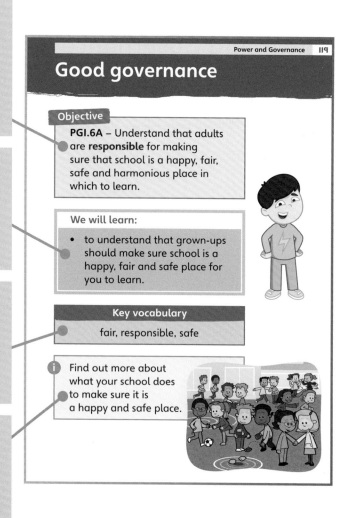

This book provides a clear structure to your learning. Each unit is based around a Global Citizenship strand and clearly focuses on the mastery of key objectives. These objectives are set out at the start of each session, along with the opportunity to reflect on what you have learned at the end of each session in the unit.

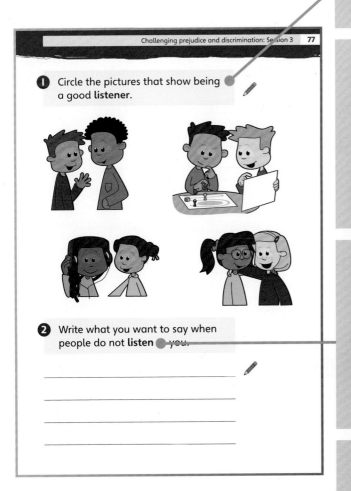

Challenging prejudice and discrimination: Session 3   77

❶ Circle the pictures that show being a good **listener**.

❷ Write what you want to say when people do not **listen** to you.

Instruction
Read this carefully to know what to do.

Activity
You might need to write or draw an answer, circle pictures or words, or tick or match answers.

Key vocabulary
Some tricky words are in **bold**. Find out what these mean in the Glossary at the back of the book.

You might have a question to think about or discuss with a Talk Partner or adult.

Meet the mascots!

Global Citizens!

We are all part of a Global Community – we are Global Citizens!

In this book you will meet lots of different people. Some may look like you and some may look different. Every one of them has a lot in common with you though! Some may be from a part of the world you know, or from a city, town or village just like yours.

The same issues affect all of us. In this book they will help you learn what you can do to make good changes both locally and globally.

You will also meet, and learn about, some of the different animals which may need our help to meet global challenges.

The Giant Panda

Giant Pandas live in China and are very rare. People are trying to protect their homes now. Protecting their homes also helps a lot of other animals.

The Malayan Tapir

Malayan Tapirs are found in parts of South-East Asia. Young tapirs have stripes but lose them as they grow. They are endangered and need our help!

The Golden Jackal

Golden Jackals live in parts of Africa. Because there are so many of them, they often meet people. We need to learn how to live safely alongside this animal.

The African Elephant

The African Elephant is the world's largest land animal! They have been hunted a lot but more and more people are learning about how they can be protected.

The Sumatran Orangutan

The Sumatran Orangutan lives in the trees of tropical rainforests. They are very endangered. In many places, the trees they live in are being cut down for people to use the wood.

Justice and injustice

Objective

SJEI.IA – Recognise **fairness** and **unfairness** in everyday situations.

We will learn:

- what is fair
- what is unfair
- about what we can do to make things fairer.

Key vocabulary

fair, fairness, feel, sharing, unfair, unfairness

ⓘ You are sharing out sweets between you and your friends. You all get the same number of sweets. Is that fair?

You give yourself more sweets than you give to your friends. Is that fair?

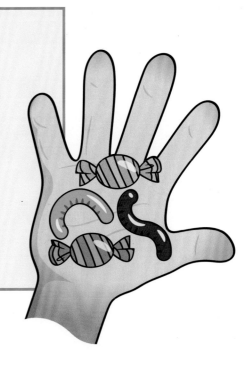

1 Draw a picture to show how you **feel** when things are **fair**.

2 Draw a picture to show how you feel when things are **unfair**.

3 Draw a line to match the examples with the words.

Keeping all the toys

Taking turns

Sharing

Eating all the sweets

fair

unfair

unfair

fair

4 When can you be fair?
Write **one** example in each box.

```
┌─────────────────────┐          ┌─────────────────────┐
│                     │          │                     │
│  _____  │          │  _____  │
└─────────────────────┘          └─────────────────────┘
```

↖   ↗

being fair

↙   ↘

```
┌─────────────────────┐          ┌─────────────────────┐
│                     │          │                     │
│  _____  │          │  _____  │
└─────────────────────┘          └─────────────────────┘
```

What new things have you learned?

What had you not thought about before?

Wealth and poverty in society

Objective

SJEI.IB – Appreciate that wealth does not make you a better person.

We will learn:

- to understand that we are all **equally** important
- that just because someone has more money than another person, it does not mean they are a better person.

Key vocabulary

equally, kind, rich, unkind

i Everyone deserves to be treated in the same way, no matter how much money they have.

1 Look at the picture. Draw a line to match the sentences to the people in the picture.

Who do you think has the most **money**?

Who do you think is the kindest?

Do you have to be **rich** to be a good person? Circle your answer. **Yes** **No**

2 Draw a picture of something you could do to be a good person.

3 Draw a picture of a time when you were **kind** or shared something with someone else.

4 Draw a line to match the pictures with the words. One has been done for you.

kind   **unkind**

unkind   kind

What new things have you learned?

What had you not thought about before?

Equality of opportunity

Objective

SJEI.IC – Appreciate that not everyone likes the same things or wants to be treated the same.

We will learn:

- that it is fine for people to be different
- that it is fine if we like different things to our friends.

Key vocabulary

different, same

i   Think about the things you enjoy doing, eating and playing. It does not matter if your friends like different things!

1 Draw pictures of **different** foods you like and foods you do not like.

I like	I do not like

2 Draw a picture of something that you and your friends enjoy doing together.

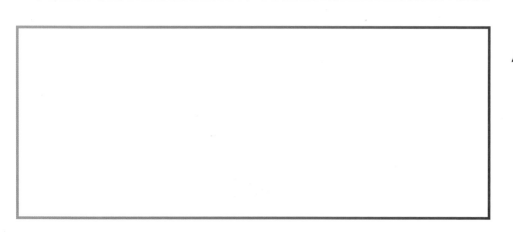

3 What can you find out about the games a Talk Partner likes to play? Ask a Talk Partner the question and draw their answers below.

What games do you like to play?

4 Talk to people in your family and find out what foods they like.
Do you all like the **same** foods?
Circle your answer.   **Yes**   **No**

5 Fill in your favourite food and then **three** other people's favourite foods. Draw a picture of each person's favourite food below.

My favourite food	_____'s favourite food
_____'s favourite food	**_____'s favourite food**

What new things have you learned?

What had you not thought about before?

Challenging injustice

Objective

SJEI.ID – Be aware of right and wrong.

We will learn:

- the difference between right and wrong
- to **admit** when we have done something wrong and say sorry.

Key vocabulary

admit, fault, hurt, mistake, sorry

ℹ It is important to say sorry if you know you have made a mistake or upset someone.

Sorry.

1 Draw a picture of how you feel when you have done something wrong.

2 Draw a picture of how you feel when someone says **sorry** to you.

3 If you make a **mistake** and upset someone, what should you say?
Tick **one** box.

☐   It is not my **fault**.

☐   I did not mean to.

☐   I am sorry.

☐   I could not help it.

4 Draw a line to match the examples with the words.

Breaking a friend's toy and then hiding it	right
Telling your teacher when you have done something wrong	wrong
Grabbing a book from someone who is reading it	right
Saying sorry when you have **hurt** a friend	wrong

What new things have you learned?

What had you not thought about before?

Conflicts in the community

Objective

PCI.4A – Be able to share things and play with others **peacefully** and **cooperatively**.

We will learn:

- to play and share things **together**
- to make everyone feel happy and included.

Key vocabulary

cooperatively, peacefully, together

ⓘ Everyone can be happy if we include everyone and share as we play!

1 Think of times when you have shared something. Circle the pictures of things you have shared.

2 Draw a picture to show how you might feel if you are left out of a game.

3 Draw a picture to show a time a friend shared something with you.

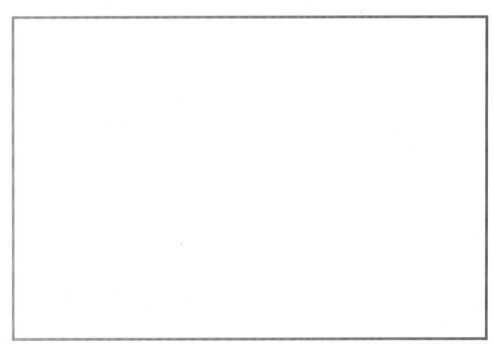

4 Draw a line to the happy or sad face from each box to show how it makes you feel.

When you play a game with new friends

When someone pushes ahead of you

When people take turns

When friends leave you out

What new things have you learned?

What had you not thought about before?

Resolving conflicts peacefully

Objective

PCI.4B – Know how to share, care for others and be a good friend.

We will learn:

- how to share
- how to **care** for others
- how to be a good friend.

Key vocabulary

care, listener, unkind

i How do you feel when your friends include you in their games and share with you?

1 Draw a picture to show something you can do to be a good friend.

2 Draw a picture of someone who is a good friend.

3 Circle the words that describe a good friend.

kind   leaves people out   shares

does not share   **unkind**   friendly

caring   good **listener**

4 Write a sentence about what makes someone a good friend.

_____

_____

_____

_____

What new things have you learned?

What had you not thought about before?

Conflicts around the world

Objective

PCI.4C – Know that sometimes people fight and that they can become friends again.

We will learn:

- that sometimes people can **fight** and fall out but they can still become friends again.

Key vocabulary

fall out, fault, fight, hurt, make up, sorry

ⓘ It is important to always make up with your friends if you fall out.

1 Do you sometimes **fall out** with a friend? Draw a picture of how it makes you feel.

2 Draw a picture of how you feel when you **make up** with a friend.

3 Imagine you have fallen out with a friend. Draw them a picture and write a message to them below to show that you want to make friends again.

4 How can you make friends again?
Circle the things you can say.

I am **sorry**.

I will not do that again.

It was not my **fault**.

I like being your friend.

I did not mean to **hurt** you.

I could not help it.

What new things have you learned?

What had you not thought about before?

Planet Earth

Objective

SDI.7A – Know about the **world**: its physical features and its wealth of living creatures and plants.

We will learn:

- about planet Earth
- about the land and sea
- about the amazing animals and **plants** that live here.

Key vocabulary

creature, home, planet Earth, plant, sea, world

Our planet is an amazing place to explore! Find out more about the amazing living things found on **planet Earth**.

1 Draw lines to match these animals to where they live. One has been done for you.

land

sea

2 Choose **one** of the **creatures** from Activity I and draw it in its **home**.

3 Write the names of **five** creatures that live in your country.

1 _____

2 _____

3 _____

4 _____

5 _____

4 Choose a creature and write a sentence to say why you like it.

_____

_____

_____

_____

_____

What new things have you learned?

What had you not thought about before?

Connecting with nature

Objective

SDI.7B – Be able to find beauty in nature.

We will learn:

- to find all the beautiful things in nature.

Key vocabulary

nature, pattern

 What makes something beautiful? Take a look at all the beauty in **nature** around you!

1 Draw a picture of snowflakes falling from the sky.

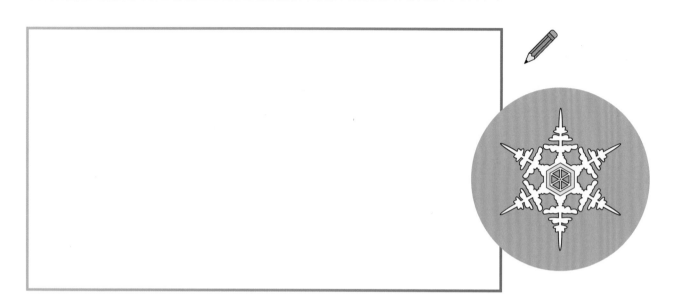

2 Draw a picture of a natural object you might find where you live, such as a leaf, pebble or pine cone.

3 Draw a line to match the **pattern** with the natural object.

4 Draw a line to the boxes to show what you could use a magnifying glass for.

to look at something more closely.

to make something look smaller.

I could use a magnifying glass

to hear more clearly.

to look at the patterns on things.

to make something look bigger.

What new things have you learned?

What had you not thought about before?

Exploring nature (Greater Depth)

Objective

SDI.7A and SDI.7B – Explore the local environment and encourage curiosity about nature.

We will learn:

- to explore our local environment
- to find out more about **nature**.

Key vocabulary

creature, nature

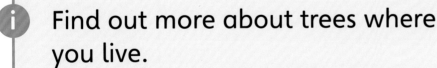

ⓘ Find out more about trees where you live.

1 Look at three different types of tree in your area. Do they all have the same shape? Which one do you like the best? Draw it.

2   Did you see any **creatures** in the trees? Draw **one** creature.

3   Ask a Talk Partner what they know about trees. Write or draw their answers.

4   Write what **you** know about trees?

5 Circle the words that are part of a tree.

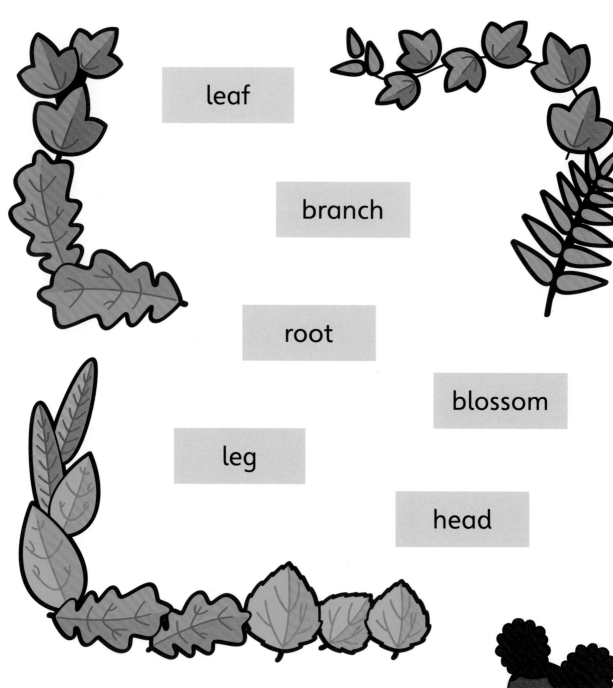

leaf

branch

root

blossom

leg

head

What new things have you learned?

What had you not thought about before?

Biodiversity and habitat loss

Objective

SDI.7C – Know that there are many different creatures and plants on the Earth that need different habitats.

We will learn:

- that all the animals and plants on planet Earth need different places to live in.

Key vocabulary

creature, habitat, plant

i Animals and **plants** all need different places to live to give them what they need. Find out more about their different habitats.

1 Tigers live in forest **habitats**.
Draw a picture of a different wild animal in its habitat.

2 Draw a picture of a pond and the **creatures** that live in it.

3 What creatures can you think of that live in the sea?

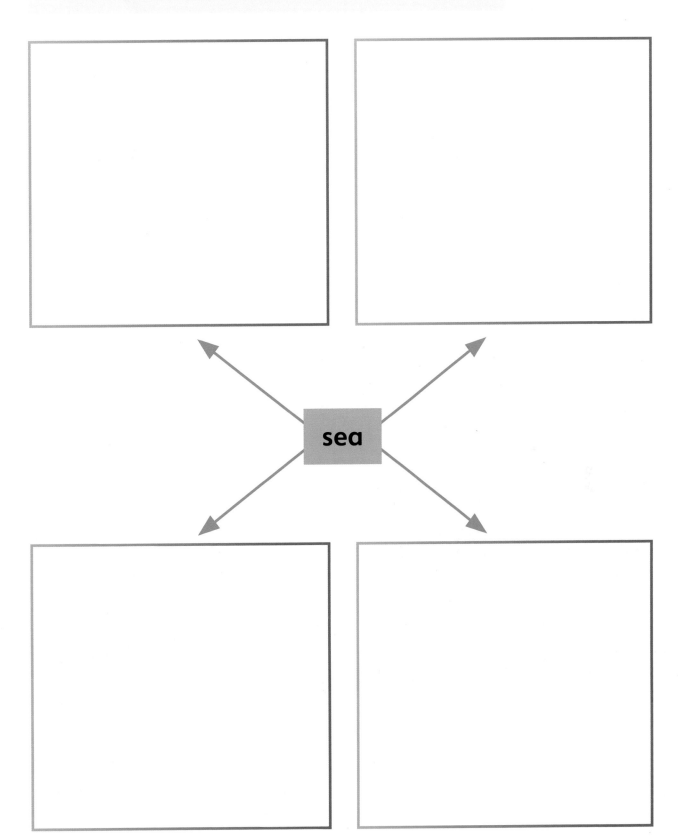

sea

4 Draw a line to match the creatures with their correct habitats.
One has been done for you.

flower   forest

river   desert

What new things have you learned?

What had you not thought about before?

Climate change

Objective

SDI.7D – Know about different types of weather and how to respond appropriately.

We will learn:

- about different types of weather
- what to do when we have different weather.

Key vocabulary

weather

ⓘ What is the weather like where you are today? Think about what you need in this weather and in different weather.

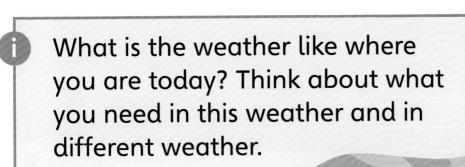

1 Draw a picture of your favourite **weather**.

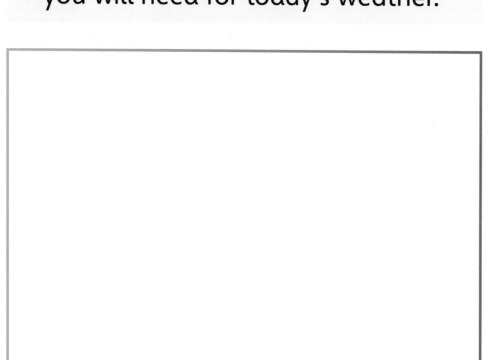

2 Draw a picture of all the things you will need for today's weather.

3 How many different kinds of
weather can you think of?
Draw a picture in each box.

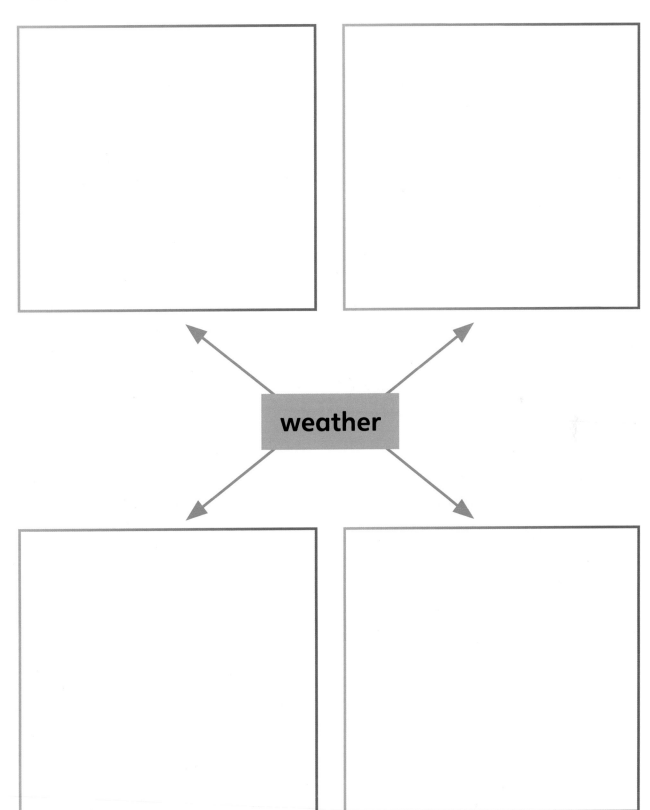

weather

4 Draw a line to match the clothes to the weather pictures.

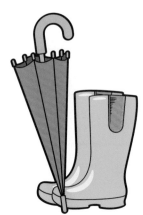

What new things have you learned?

What had you not thought about before?

Energy, pollution, waste and recycling

Objective

SDI.7E – Try not to waste things.

We will learn:

- that we must not waste things.

Key vocabulary

recycle, reuse, waste

ⓘ Think about what you can do to stop wasting things. What can you reuse or recycle?

1 Circle the things that you could **reuse**.

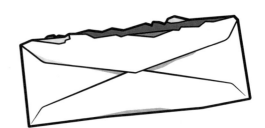

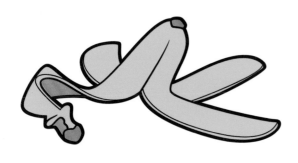

2 Talk to your friends and family about what they do to reuse things and stop **waste**. Draw one of the things they reuse.

3 What can you reuse yogurt pots for? Draw a picture.

4 Draw a poster telling people how to **recycle**.

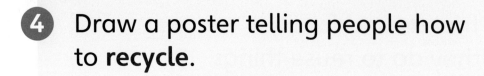

What new things have you learned?

What had you not thought about before?

The future of our planet

Objective

SDI.7F – Appreciate that we live on the Earth and that it is **precious**, unique and worthy of awe and wonder.

We will learn:

- that we live on a special and **unique** planet
- that we should look after our planet.

Key vocabulary

alien, planet Earth, precious, sea, unique

ℹ Do you know what planet Earth looks like from space? Find out more about our amazing planet!

1 Colour the picture of **planet Earth**. Use different colours to show the land and the **sea**.

2 What do you think is so special about planet Earth? Draw a picture in each box.

What is so special about planet Earth?

3 Circle the things you think an **alien** visiting planet Earth would find the most amazing and beautiful.

Write a sentence about your favourite picture.

_____

_____

What new things have you learned?

What had you not thought about before?

Who am I? (Greater Depth)

Objective

IDI.2A – Be able to find connections with people I meet.

We will learn:

- how to make **connections** with the people around us.

Key vocabulary

connection

You can make new friends by finding out what you have in common with the people around you.

1 Draw a picture of a game or sport enjoyed by you and two people you know.

2 Draw some things that are your favourite colour and colour them in.

3 Talk to your family and friends and find out what their favourite animal is in the chart below. Keep a tally under each picture to see which animal most people like.

4 Write a sentence about a new friend you have made.

_____

_____

_____

_____

_____

Draw three things that you both like.

5 Ask some other people what food they like. Write the names of anyone who likes the same food as you.

_____

_____

_____

_____

_____

6 Draw a picture of the food that you and other people like.

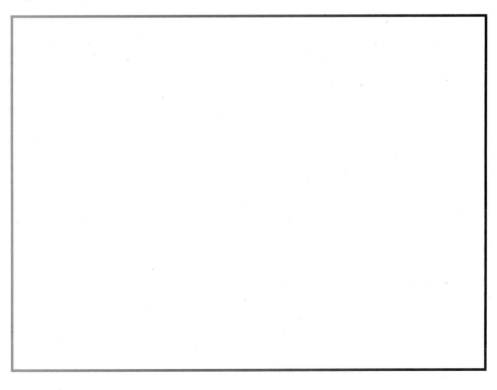

7 Draw a picture of one of your friends or a member of your family in the middle. Then draw all the things you know they like around them.

8   Write the names of people you know who match the descriptions.

A friend who likes the same toys as you

A friend who likes different toys to you

A friend who likes different food to you

A friend who likes the same food as you

What new things have you learned?

What had you not thought about before?

Humankind: all equal; all different

Objective

IDI.2B – Show an interest in and a curiosity about others.

We will learn:

- to be interested in and show **respect** for other people who are different to you.

Key vocabulary

different, respect, same

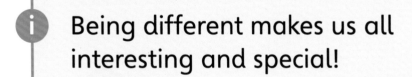

(i) Being different makes us all interesting and special!

1 Think of one of your friends.
Write **two** things that are the **same**
about both of you and **two** things
that are **different**.

_____

_____

_____

_____

2 What is your favourite book?
Draw a picture of one of the
characters in the book and share
it with a Talk Partner.

3 Talk to your friends and find out what their favourite activity at school is from the headings on the chart. Keep a tally below to see which activity the most people like.

Playing games	Reading books	Painting pictures	Doing maths

4 Choose one of your friends and write their name. Then circle the words that show what is the same about you and underline the words that show what is different about you.

My friend's name is:

_____

eyes	hair

shoes	favourite food

favourite game	school bag

What new things have you learned?

What had you not thought about before?

Challenging prejudice and discrimination

Objective

IDI.2C – Know how to be a good listener.

We will learn:

- how to be a good listener.

Key vocabulary

listen, listener, respect, safe

ⓘ We all feel better when people listen to us.

1 Circle the pictures that show being a good **listener**.

2 Write what you want to say when people do not **listen** to you.

3 Draw four things that are interesting to listen to. Draw a picture in each box.

We can listen to...

4 Draw lines to show the reasons why we need to listen to each other.

...so we know the rules.

...so we can stay **safe**.

...so we can leave people out.

It is important to listen...

...so everyone can join in.

...to show **respect** to other people.

...so we can make lots of noise.

What new things have you learned?

What had you not thought about before?

People and places around the world

GII.3A – Understand my home and **local** place within the wider world.

We will learn:

- to understand where our **home** is in the world.

Key vocabulary

city, countryside, home, local, map, mountain, world

i How well do you know the area where you live? Where is it in the **world**?

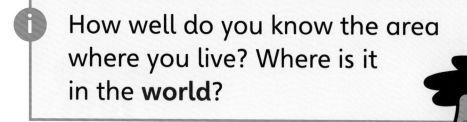

1 Draw a line to match the pictures to the words.

countryside

map

city

globe

2 Draw a picture showing some of the buildings on the street where you live.

3 Have you ever travelled to a different city or country? What can you remember from your visit? Draw a picture showing what you can remember.

4 Add the correct word to each sentence.

globe   address   country

My _____ tells you where my house and street are.

You can find the country where you live on a _____ .

Sara lives in a small _____ with many **mountains** and one big city.

What new things have you learned?

What had you not thought about before?

Global trade, ethics, production and consumption

Objective

GII.3B – Know that we rely on many different people in many different countries to produce the things we buy.

We will learn:

- that we need many different people in many different **countries** to make all the things we **buy**.

Key vocabulary

buy, countries, factory, world

ⓘ Did you know that the things you eat, drink and use every day come from all over the **world**?

1 Draw a picture of some of the food you have eaten today. Where did the food come from?

2 Draw a picture of a toy or game that was made in a different country.

3 Look in your kitchen and find four items of food. With help, find out where the food was grown or packaged. Draw a picture of the items and write where they are from.

This comes from

_____.

This comes from

_____.

This comes from

_____.

This comes from

_____.

4 Draw a line to show where each item comes from. One has been done for you.

farm

factory

What new things have you learned?

What had you not thought about before?

Global wealth and poverty

Objective

GII.3C – Be aware of money and what it is used for.

We will learn:

- about money
- what we use money for.

Key vocabulary

buy, money, sell, spend

ℹ Find out more about how we use money when we buy and **sell** things.

1 Draw a picture of the **money** you use to **buy** things.

2 What was the last thing you bought or someone bought for you? Draw a picture of it.

3 How many things can you think of that you can buy in a shop? Draw a picture in each box.

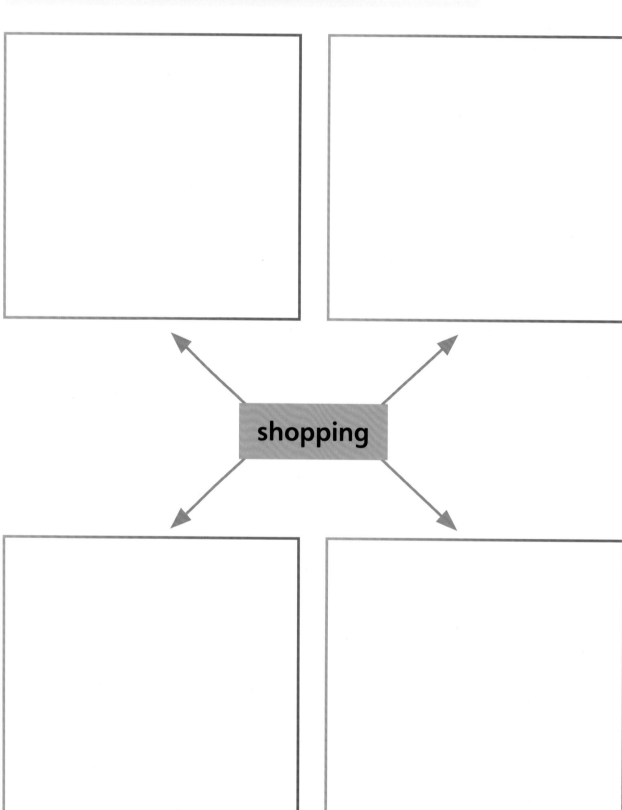

shopping

4 Circle the pictures showing where you can **spend** money.

What new things have you learned?

What had you not thought about before?

Information, technology and communication

Objective

GII.3D – Know about some of the uses of digital technology.

We will learn:

- about the different ways we can communicate with other people.

Key vocabulary

communicate, mobile phone, technology

ⓘ Find out why it is important to keep in touch with other people and how we can do it in different ways.

1 How many ways can you think of to **communicate** with each other? Draw a line to the things people use to communicate.

ways to communicate

2   Draw a picture showing a way you can communicate with other people.

3   Draw a picture of someone you communicate with using **technology**.

4 Draw a line to match the pictures with the words. One has been done for you.

tablet

games console

computer

mobile phone

What new things have you learned?

What had you not thought about before?

Global health, food and well-being

Objective

GII.3E – Know how to keep clean, safe and well.

We will learn:

- how to keep clean, **safe** and well.

Key vocabulary

healthy, safe

ⓘ Think about what you can do to keep yourself clean and healthy.

1 Draw a picture to show the items
you need to keep your teeth clean.

2 Draw a picture to show the items
you need to keep your hands clean.

3   Circle **Yes** or **No** after the sentences.

We wash our hands after we have been playing in the garden.	Yes No
We wash our hands before we eat our lunch.	Yes No
We wash our hands before we go for a walk.	Yes No
We wash our hands after we have been to the toilet.	Yes No
We wash our hands while we are reading a book.	Yes No

4   Draw a picture showing how you wash your hands.

5 Draw a line to match the examples with the words.

healthy

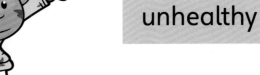
unhealthy

healthy

unhealthy

healthy

What new things have you learned?

What had you not thought about before?

Understanding rights

HRI.5A – Understand what we need to be happy, healthy and safe and how this relates to our rights.

We will learn:

- what we all need to be happy and healthy
- that we all have the right to join in.

Key vocabulary

healthy, home, rights, safe

i Find out what your **rights** are and why they are important.

1 All children have the right to have a **home**. Draw a picture of your home here.

2 All children have the right to be looked after when they are unwell. Draw a picture of someone looking after you when you are unwell.

3 One of your rights is the right to a name.

Write your name in the box. Draw pictures of your favourite things around it.

4 Draw a line to match the pictures with the rights.

A right to be **healthy**

A right to a home

A right to be **safe**

A right to a name

What new things have you learned?

What had you not thought about before?

Violation of rights

Objective

HRI.5B – Understand that no one should hurt you in any way.

We will learn:

- that no one should hurt you in any way.

Key vocabulary

hurt, safe

i It is your right to be kept safe and not to be hurt.

1 Draw a picture of a time you were **hurt**. What happened?

2 Write the name of someone who makes you feel **safe**. Draw a picture of their face.

3 Circle the people you could speak to if you saw someone getting hurt at school.

a teacher   a friend   a parent

a stranger   a member of staff

4 Draw a picture in each box to show the people and things that make you feel safe.

What makes me feel safe?

What new things have you learned?

What had you not thought about before?

Refugees, asylum seekers and internally displaced people (Greater Depth)

Objective

HRI.5C – Have ability and desire to make friends with people whose appearance, language or belief is different from one's own.

We will learn:

- to be happy making friends with people who look different to you, speak a different language or who have different beliefs to you.

Key vocabulary

language, together

ⓘ Just because someone is different to you, it does not mean you cannot be friends!

1 What is your name? Ask your family if your name has any special meaning. Write the meaning and draw a picture of yourself.

_____

_____

_____

_____

_____

2 Ask a friend who gave them their name and why? Write their name and draw a picture of them.

3 Draw a picture of what it feels like when people call you the wrong name.

4 Circle the things you can learn from someone who is from a different place to you.

a new game

a new **language**

a new joke

a new way of dancing

a new song

a new recipe

5 Draw a picture to show you and your friend learning something **together**.

6 Talk to an adult and see if they have ever visited a new place. What was it like? Draw a picture showing them in their new place.

7 Draw a picture in each box to show how you can make someone new in your class feel welcome.

How can I welcome a new friend?

What new things have you learned?

What had you not thought about before?

Rights defenders

Objective

HRI.5D – Have ability and desire to behave kindly and respectfully towards others.

We will learn:

- how to **behave** kindly and **respectfully** to other people.

Key vocabulary

behave, hurt, kind, listen, respect, respectfully

ⓘ The best thing you can be is kind!

1 Draw a picture of someone you know who is **kind**. Write their name underneath.

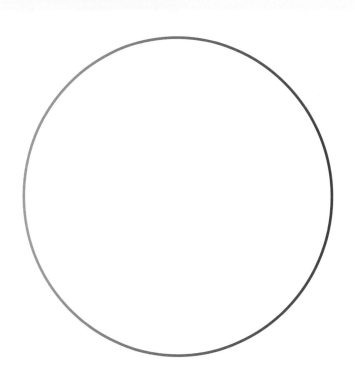

2 Draw a picture of how you feel when someone is kind to you.

3 Circle the words that describe someone who is kind.

friendly

listens to me

shares

lets me join in

gentle

leaves me out

ignores me

caring

hurts me

respects me

4 Draw a picture of a time someone was kind to you.

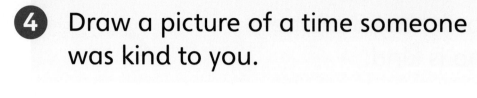

What new things have you learned?

What had you not thought about before?

Good governance

Objective

PGI.6A – Understand that adults are **responsible** for making sure that school is a happy, fair, safe and harmonious place in which to learn.

We will learn:

- to understand that grown-ups should make sure school is a happy, fair and safe place for you to learn.

Key vocabulary

fair, responsible, safe

ⓘ Find out more about what your school does to make sure it is a happy and safe place.

1 Can you think of something your teacher does to make you feel **safe**? Write what they do here.

_____

_____

_____

_____

_____

2 Draw a picture showing you in a place where you feel safe.

3   Choose **one** word for each sentence.
Write the word in the gap.

safe   fair   happy

I smile when I am _____.

I feel _____ when the

grown-ups at school look after me.

I like my teachers. They are

_____ to everyone.

What new things have
you learned?

What had you not thought
about before?

Participation and inclusion

Objective

PG1.6B – Know how and when to participate: listen carefully, take turns in speaking, and enable your own voice to be heard.

We will learn:

- how and when to join in, to listen and take turns speaking.

Key vocabulary

fair, listen, respect, safe

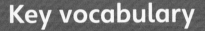
Think about how you feel when it is your turn to speak.
Find out more about why it is important to **listen** to everyone.

1 Write the names of the people you have listened to today.

_____

_____

_____

2 Draw a picture of someone who has listened to you today. Write about what you told them.

_____

_____

3 How do you feel when you do
not get a chance to speak?
Write about how it makes you feel
and draw a picture to show it.

_____

_____

_____

_____

4   Why do you think everyone should
     have a turn to speak?
     Tick **three** boxes.

☐   So we can stay **safe**

☐   Because it is **fair**

☐   So there is lots of noise

☐   To show **respect** for each other

☐   So everyone can join in

☐   So we can leave people out

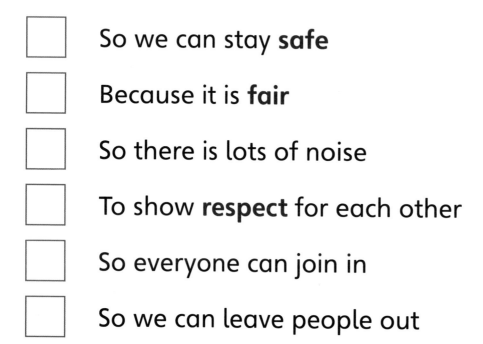

What new things have
you learned?

What had you not thought
about before?

admit	to agree that something is true or that someone else is right
alien	different from what you are used to, especially in a way that is difficult to understand or accept
behave	to not do things that upset others
buy	to get something by paying money for it
care	the process of looking after someone
city	a big town
communicate	how people share information or express their thoughts and feelings
connect	to join two or more things together
connection	something that joins two or more things together
cooperatively	the way you work with someone else
countries	areas of land with boundaries and people who live there
countryside	land that is outside cities and towns

creature	living things such as an animal, fish or insect, but not a plant
different	not the same
equally	having the same rights and opportunities as everyone else
factory	a building where goods are produced in large amounts
fair	treating everyone in a way that is right
fairness	treating everyone in the same way or with kindness
fall out	to have a disagreement with a friend
fault	something that is not perfect
feel	to have an emotion, such as anger, sadness or happiness
fight	to be cross with someone in a physical or emotional way
habitat	the natural home of a plant or animal
healthy	being well

home	the place where you live
hurt	to feel pain in a part of your body or in your emotions
jobs	something you do to earn money
kind	being thoughtful to someone or something
language	written or spoken words used by people
listen	to pay attention to what someone is saying or to a sound that you can hear
listener	someone who pays attention to what someone is saying
local	near to where you are
make up	to become friendly with someone again after you have had an argument
map	a drawing of an area, for example a city or country, which shows its features, such as roads or mountains

mistake	something done the wrong way, or an opinion or statement that is incorrect
mobile phone	a phone you can carry with you
money	what you earn by working and can use to buy things
mountain	a very tall and big hill
nature	everything in the physical world that is not controlled by humans, such as wild plants and animals, earth and rocks, and the weather
notes	something that you write down to remind you of something
oceans	a big area of water
pattern	shapes or colours that are repeated
peacefully	behaving in a quiet and calm way
phone	a piece of technology that allows a person to speak with another person without being in the same place
planet Earth	the planet we live on

plant	a living thing that has leaves and roots and grows in earth, especially one that is smaller than a tree
precious	something or someone that is valuable and important
produce	food or other things that have been grown or produced to be sold
recycle	the process of treating used objects or materials so that they can be used again
respect	a feeling of admiring someone or what they do, especially because of their personal qualities, knowledge or skills
respectfully	feeling or showing respect
responsible	being in charge of someone or something and making sure they are looked after
reuse	to use something again
rich	having a lot of money and valuable possessions

rights	something that you are allowed to do or have
rubbish	items that are no longer needed and have been thrown away
safe	not in danger of being harmed, lost or stolen
same	not different
sea	a big area of water
sharing	to have or use something with other people
sorry	feeling ashamed or unhappy about something you have done
sound	something that you hear, or what can be heard
technology	new machines, equipment and ways of doing things that are based on modern knowledge about science and computers
texture	the way a surface or material feels, especially how smooth or rough it is
together	to do something with at least one other person

town	a large area with houses, shops, offices and other buildings where people live and work. It is smaller than a city and larger than a village
unfair	not treating everyone in a way that is right
unfairness	not treating everyone in the same way or with unkindness
unique	of which only one or very few exists; something that is rare
unkind	treating people in a way that makes them unhappy or upset
waste	when something such as money or skills or an object are not used in a way that is effective, useful or sensible
waterproofs	not allowing water to enter
weather	weather can include rain, snow, storms, wind, fog, sunshine
world	the society that we live in, the way people behave and the kind of life we have; the planet we live on